ALSO FROM JOE BOOKS

Published simultaneously in the United States and Canada by Joe Books Ltd,
489 College Street, Suite 203, Toronto, ON M6G 1A5.

www.joebooks.com

First Joe Books edition: August 2018

Print ISBN: 978-1-77391-127-4

Library and Archives Canada Cataloguing in Publication
information is available upon request.

Printed and bound in Canada
1 3 5 7 9 10 8 6 4 2

Disney

GRAVITY FALLS

JOE BOOKS LTD

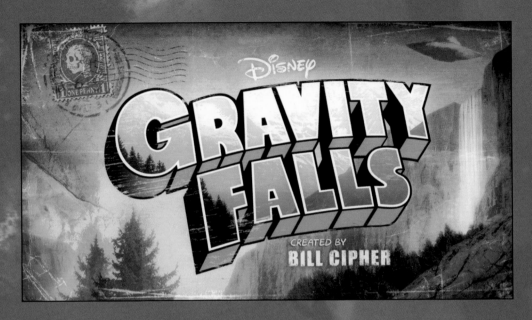

WEIRDMAGEDDON
PART 1

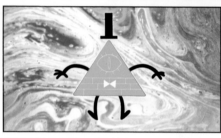

NOW SEE HERE, YOU UNHOLY TRIANGLE FELLA!

AS MAYOR, I STRONGLY URGE YOU TO GET--GET ON OUTTA HERE!

COOL

YEAH, THINGS WITH ONE EYE ARE WEIRD.

WE DON'T LIKE OUT-OF-TOWNERS!

WE PUNCH WHAT WE *DON'T* UNDERSTAND!

I WOULD JUST LIKE TO SAY THAT, AS A RICH CAPITALIST, I WELCOME YOUR TYRANNICAL RULE. PERHAPS I CAN BE ONE OF YOUR...HORSEMEN OF THE APOCALYPSE?

DAD!

NOT NOW, SWEETIE. THE GROWN-UPS ARE TALKING.

13

IT'S TIME WE DO A LITTLE REDECORATING.

I COULD REALLY USE A CASTLE OF SOME KIND.

AND HOW ABOUT SOME BUBBLES OF PURE MADNESS?

AAAUGHHHH!

THIS PARTY NEVER STOPS! TIME IS DEAD AND MEANING HAS NO MEANING.

EXISTENCE IS UPSIDE DOWN AND I REIGN SUPREME!

WHHRRHAAAA

WELCOME ONE AND ALL TO *WEIRDMAGEDDON!*

SO THIS IS HOW THE WORLD ENDS.

NOT WITH A BANG, BUT WITH A ⁚BOOP, BOOP⁚.

WEIRDMAGEDDON.

AAH!

WHOA-- AGH!

HEY, WE'RE SCAMPERING HERE!

MOVE IT, STRETCH!

THE RIFT IS SHATTERED--BILL'S WORLD IS SPILLING INTO OURS.

AND EVERY MINUTE, HIS POWERS GROW STRONGER.

BUT BEING A HERO MEANS FIGHTING BACK EVEN WHEN IT SEEMS *IMPOSSIBLE.*

WILL YOU FOLLOW ME?

TO THE ENDS OF THE EARTH.

GOOD, BECAUSE THAT'S WHERE WE'RE HEADING.

MYSTERY HACK

YOU ALSO MIGHT WANNA STEP INSIDE.

GASP

MYSTERY SHACK.

THUNK
THUNK

HEY!

THAT'S IT, GOAT. IT'S TIME I THREW YOU OFF THIS PROPERTY FOR GOOD!

ON SECOND THOUGHT, I'M GONNA RUN LIKE A COWARD NOW.

MRRAAGGHHHHHH.

AAAUUGHHH!

DOWNTOWN.

RAUGH! FREEDOM! FREEDOM TO PUNCH.

20

PRISON.

OKAY, INMATES, TIME TO REVIEW YOUR FINGER PAINTINGS.

GOOD...

...NICE...

-GASP- UGH. GIDEON, DOES THIS LOOK LIKE SOMEONE WHO'S READY TO RE-ENTER SOCIETY?

REVENGE

LOVE →

GIDEON'S UNAPPRECIATED IN HIS TIME!

OH, GHOST-EYES, YOU'RE MAKIN' ME BLUSH.

GIDEON MAKES PRISON LIFE WORTH LIVING.

GIDEON! GIDEON!

22

DOWNTOWN.

READY TO CAUSE SOME HAVOC, BOYS?

AH, MY QUANTUM DESTABILIZER.

EXPERIMENT 618

I'VE BEEN WAITING A LONG TIME TO USE THIS.

WE'RE ONLY GONNA HAVE ONE CHANCE TO TAKE THIS SHOT.

STEADY... STEADY...AND--

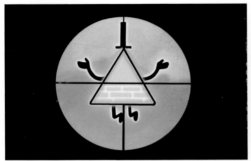

WA-HA-HA-HA-HOO-HOO! I'M ALIVE NOW.

PTHEW

AUGH!

OH, NO!

WELL, WELL, WELL, AND HERE I THOUGHT TODAY COULDN'T GET ANY *BETTER!*

Fzzz

THOOOOM

GREAT-UNCLE FORD!

UGH. DIPPER, TAKE MY JOURNALS!

LISTEN, I KNOW OF ONE OTHER WAY TO DEFEAT BILL.

IT'S--OH, NO! DIPPER, RUN! GET DOWN!

GOOD OL' SIX FINGERS. I'VE BEEN WAITING AN *ETERNITY* TO HAVE A CHAT FACE TO FACE.

WAAH!

EVERYONE, THIS ARMAGEDDON WOULDN'T BE POSSIBLE WITHOUT HELP FROM OUR FRIEND HERE! GIVE HIM A SIX-FINGERED HAND!

WOO! YEAH!

THIS BRAINIAC IS THE ONE WHO BUILT THE PORTAL IN THE FIRST PLACE!

AW, DON'T LOOK SO SOUR, FORDSY, IT'S NOT TOO LATE TO JOIN ME.

WITH THAT EXTRA FINGER, YOU'D FIT RIGHT IN WITH MY FREAKS.

I'LL DIE BEFORE I JOIN YOU! I KNOW YOUR WEAKNESS, BILL!

OH, YEAH? AND I KNOW A *RIDDLE!* WHY DID THE OLD MAN DO THIS?

THIS?

FZzz

÷GASP÷

26

27

NO! THE JOURNALS!

NOT MUCH OF A THREAT NOW, ARE YOU? NOW, CAN ANYONE REMIND ME WHY WE CAME HERE?

TO GET WEIRD!

THAT'S RIGHT! VIP PARTY AT THE FEARAMID! OH, AND 8 BALL, TEETH?

YOU'VE EARNED A TREAT, HAVE THE KID FOR A SNACK.

HEH-HEH-HEH!

HUH?

HENCHMANIACS, ROLL OUT!

HEH-HEH-HEH-HEH.

29

WE ARE DAY THREE IN THIS STRANGE CATACLYSMIC EVENT, WHICH SOME ARE CALLING "WEIRDMAGEDDON" OR THE "ODDPOCALYPSE."

WEATHER TODAY CALLS FOR BLACK CLOUDS, BLOOD RAIN, AND FREQUENT SHOWERS OF EYEBALL BATS TURNING PEOPLE INTO STONE.

I'M SHANDRA JIMENEZ AND I ATE A RAT FOR DINNER.

AH!
≻PANT≺

MABEL, IT'S ME. SO FAR I'VE ELUDED CAPTURE, BUT I HAVEN'T BEEN ABLE TO FIND YOU OR STAN ANYWHERE.

I DON'T KNOW IF YOU CAN HEAR ME, BUT WHEREVER YOU ARE, WHATEVER HAPPENS, I'M GOING TO FIND YOU.

STAN! MABEL!

MAYBE AT LEAST I CAN GET SOMETHING TO EAT.

THE LAST NACHOS ON EARTH.

AAH! HELP! THE NACHOS TRICKED ME!

FWIPP

DIPPER?

WENDY?

OH, NO! YOU'VE BEEN TRANSFORMED INTO SOME SORT OF TREE MONSTER!

HAH! IT'S JUST CAMOUFLAGE.

MY DAD MADE ME AND MY BROTHERS DO APOCALYPSE TRAINING EVERY YEAR INSTEAD OF CHRISTMAS.

GUESS IT'S SORT OF COOL THEIR PARANOIA PAID OFF.

FWOP

NICE! BAT MEAT.

LET ME GET THAT FOR YA.

UGH.

FWOOP

SPLAT

WENDY, I'M SO GLAD TO FIND YOU. I THOUGHT EVERYONE I KNEW WAS GONE.

HEY, HEY, IT'S OKAY. WE HAVE EACH OTHER NOW.

AND TOBY DETERMINED, WHO I ACCIDENTALLY MISTOOK FOR A MONSTER.

THIS JUST IN--

--THIS ARROW IN MY SHOULDER!

WE SHOULDN'T STAY OUT IN THE OPEN FOR TOO LONG. LET ME SHOW YOU MY HIDEOUT.

DUDE KEEP OUT

WE WERE PLAYING TRUTH OR DARE IN THE CEMETERY WHEN IT HAPPENED.

THE EYEBALLS FROZE NATE, LEE, TAMBRY, AND THOMPSON.

ROBBIE ALMOST GOT AWAY BUT HAD TO PAUSE TO TAKE A SELFIE. WHAT ABOUT YOU?

I WAS IN A FIGHT WITH MABEL WHEN IT HAPPENED.

UNCLE FORD ASKED ME TO BE HIS APPRENTICE AFTER THE SUMMER WAS OVER, BUT THAT WOULD MEAN I WOULDN'T GO BACK HOME.

IT WOULD MEAN GROWING UP WITHOUT MABEL.

OH, *DUDE.*

MABEL DIDN'T TAKE IT WELL, AND SHE RAN OFF INTO THE FOREST.

SHE COULDN'T EVEN LOOK ME IN THE EYE.

COME ON, LET'S GET SOME FRESH AIR. TOBY, YOU WATCH THE CAMP.

DON'T CALL ME "TOBY" ANYMORE. CALL ME "BODACIOUS T"!

NO ONE WILL EVER CALL YOU THAT.

AW.

36

END OF THE WORLD.

MAN, THOSE DEATH METAL ALBUM COVERS GOT IT SHOCKINGLY RIGHT.

YOU KNOW, I USED TO THINK I COULD GET OUT OF ANYTHING. BUT *THIS?*

THE JOURNALS ARE DESTROYED, FORD IS CAPTURED, AND I CAN'T FIND MY FAMILY ANYWHERE.

BILL SAID IT HIMSELF, THERE'S NO ROOM FOR HEROES OUT HERE. WE LOST.

LOOK, DUDE, IT'S NOT OVER YET. YOU'VE BEATEN BILL TWICE BEFORE.

WHY IS THIS TIME ANY DIFFERENT?

'CAUSE THEN, I HAD MABEL.

THEN YOU NEED TO GET MABEL BACK.

LOOK, THIS SUMMER, I'VE SEEN SOME AMAZING THINGS, BUT *NOTHING* AS AMAZING AS YOU AND YOUR SISTER.

I DON'T KNOW IF IT'S DUMB LUCK OR YIN AND YANG OR WHATEVER, BUT WHEN YOU TWO WORK TOGETHER THERE'S, LIKE, NOTHING YOU TWO CAN'T ACCOMPLISH.

YOU JUST NEED TO MAKE UP, AND TEAM UP, AND SAVE THE UNIVERSE.

BUT HOW WILL I EVER FIND HER?

RRAGH!

:CHOMP:

THE SHOOTING STAR FROM MABEL'S SWEATER! SHE'S IN THERE, I KNOW IT.

WHOA, IS THAT, LIKE, TWIN ESP?

NO, WE DON'T HAVE THAT.

BUT WE DO HAVE THIS THING WHERE OUR ALLERGIES TOTALLY ACT UP AT THE SAME TIME.

⸰AH...AH-CHOO⸰

MABEL NEEDS US.

FEARAMID.

SPIN THE PERSON. SPIN THE PERSON. SPIN THE PERSON.

-GASP-

WAGH!

WHOA!

-GULP-

HA-HA-HA-HA-HA! GO NUTS, GUYS! WHEN WE'RE DONE PARTYING, I UNVEIL PHASE TWO!

BILL CIPHER, YOU ARE IN VIOLATION OF THE RULES OF SPACE-TIME AND POSSESSING THE BODY OF A TIME OFFICER.

LOLPH

MY BODY IS A TEMPLE! HOW DARE YOU!

HEAR THIS, CIPHER.

UGH. *TIME BABY.*

IF YOUR RIP IN THIS DIMENSION CONTINUES, IT COULD DESTROY THE VERY FABRIC OF EXISTENCE.

SURRENDER NOW OR FACE MY TANTRUM.

OH, NO. A TANTRUM. WHATEVER WILL I DO ABOUT THAT?

43

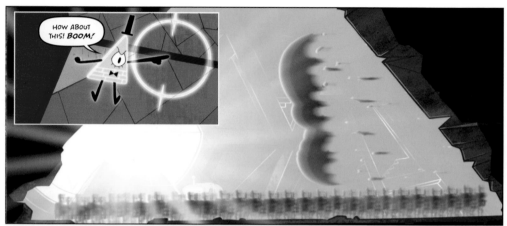

44

MEANWHILE...

THE ABANDONED AUTO MART. FREE CARS RIPE FOR THE HOT-WIRING.

WE JUST FOUND OUR RIDE TO MABEL.

I WONDER IF THEY HAVE A TANK. I'VE *ALWAYS* WANTED TO DRIVE A TANK.

I CAN'T BELIEVE THIS PLACE IS JUST ABANDONED.

OOH, AN AIR FRESHENER!

FINALLY, I'LL SMELL LIKE A PERSON! STEALY, STEALY!

FWIR

AGH!

HA! IT'S GONNA TAKE MORE THAN ONE DART TO KEEP ME FROM—

FWIP
FWIP
FWIP
FWIP
FWIP
FWIP

WHUD

45

46

URGH.

⹝OOF!⹝

WOO-WHEE! LOOK WHAT THE APOCALYPSE DRAGGED IN!

Y'ALL ARE IN A TWELVE-PIECE BUCKET OF DEEP-FRIED TROUBLE NOW.

GHOST-EYES, SPITTOON!

⹝PTUH⹝

CLANG

UGH. IT'S GIDEON.

AND HE'S GOTTEN FOLKSIER.

MY OLD PAL BILL FIGURED YOU MIGHT TRY TO RESCUE MABEL.

SO HE APPOINTED ME MASTER OF THESE WASTELANDS AND KEEPER OF THE BUBBLE.

HEH-HEH-HEH-HEH.

AH-HA-HA-HA. AND WHAT MAKES YOU THINK YOU CAN DO ALL THAT?

`CAUSE I'M A FLIPPING *CORDUROY!*

HURRGGHH!

AAAGGGGHHHHH!

GHOST-EYES! MY HENCH ANGEL!

AUGH!

GET BACK!

AAH!

GET BACK! OR I WILL DROP KICK HIM, I SWEAR.

52

OKAY, ALL WE HAVE TO DO IS OUTRACE GIDEON'S HENCHMEN, UNLOCK THE BUBBLE, SAVE MABEL, SAVE THE WORLD.

CLANG

QUICK QUESTION-- DID YOU EVER GET YOUR DRIVER'S LICENSE?

DEFINITELY NOT.

ARM!

WAAGH!

AAAHH!

‹CHOMP›

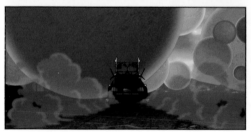

54

<TWEET, TWEET. TWEET, TWEET.>*

*FOR SOME REASON, I REALLY WANT WORMS RIGHT NOW.

<TWEET, TWEET. TWEET, TWEET.>*

*EAT WORMS! FLY SOUTH! NEST!

÷COUGH÷ EURGH! THAT WAS HORRIBLE!

HERE COMES ANOTHER ONE, DUDE! BRACE YOURSELF!

AHHHHH!

AHHHHH!

AHHHHH!

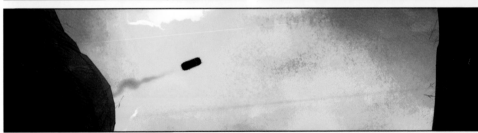

BILL'S HENCH BATS WILL BE HERE ANY MINUTE TO RETRIEVE Y'ALL.

MABEL'S MINE NOW! HA-HA-HA-HA-HA.

IS SHE?

WELL, YEAH. I HAVE HER TRAPPED. ERGO, MABEL IS *MINE!*

GIDEON, LISTEN TO ME.

IF I'VE LEARNED ANYTHING THIS SUMMER, IT'S THAT YOU CAN'T FORCE SOMEONE TO LOVE YOU.

THE BEST YOU CAN DO IS STRIVE TO BE SOMEONE WORTHY OF LOVING.

OH, I'M WORTHY OF LOVING. THESE PRISONERS LOVE ME!

YEAH! WA-HOO!

BUT MABEL DOESN'T! BECAUSE YOU'RE SELFISH. BUT YOU *CAN* CHANGE!

BILL THINKS THERE'S NO HEROES IN THIS WORLD, BUT IF WE WORK TOGETHER AND FIGHT BACK, WE CAN DEFEAT HIM.

YOU WANT TO BE MABEL'S HERO? STAND UP TO BILL AND LET US SAVE HER!

THAT'S CRAZY! D-DO YOU KNOW WHAT BILL WILL DO TO ME IF THAT HAPPENS?

WHAT, ARE YOU SCARED OF BILL?

NO, I JUST...IT'S A COMPLICATED SITUATION.

LOOK INSIDE, GIDEON. IF ALL THIS IS FOR MABEL, THEN ASK YOURSELF WHAT *MABEL* WOULD WANT YOU TO DO.

NOW WITH LESS TYPOS

LIL GIDEON'S LI'L GIRLFRIEND?

med! D
dies, this one's taken!

61

DIPPER? WILL YOU TELL HER WHAT I DID?

OF COURSE.

I HOPE YOU'RE RIGHT ABOUT THIS.

GUYS, NEW PLAN. BILL'S MINIONS ARE GONNA BE ON US IN SECONDS, BUT I'M NOT GONNA LET THAT DUMB TRIANGLE BE THE WARDEN OF ME.

Y'ALL READY FOR A GOOD OL' FASHIONED PRISON BRAWL?

WE'RE BEHIND YOU FOR LIFE, BROTHER.

FIGHTING CHILDREN IS BORING. FIGHTING A CHAOS GOD SOUNDS *FUN!*

LET'S DO THIS! HENCHMEN, ROLL OUT!

WA-HOO!

WOO-WHEE!

62

PHEW! AND I THOUGHT I WAS GONNA HAVE TO THROW DOWN.

OKAY, REMEMBER, GUYS, THIS IS A PRISON BUBBLE DESIGNED BY BILL.

WE'VE GOT TO PREPARE OURSELVES FOR WHAT WE FIND IN HERE.

WHATEVER IT IS, WE'LL DO IT TOGETHER. FOR MABEL!

FOR MABEL!

FOR MABEL.

TCHK

CLINK

63

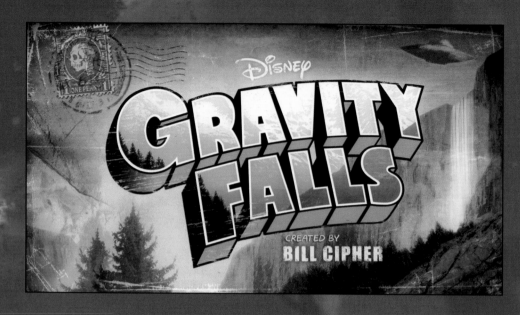

WEIRDMAGEDDON 2:
ESCAPE FROM REALITY

FEARAMID.

CLINK
CLINK

LADIES! GENTLEMEN! THAT CREATURE WITH, LIKE, EIGHTY-SEVEN DIFFERENT FACES.

EIGHTY-EIGHT DIFFERENT FACES!

WHOA, SORRY. TOUCHY SUBJECT.

ANYWAYS, IT'S BEEN FUN TURNING GRAVITY FALLS INSIDE OUT, ROUNDING UP ALL ITS TERRIFIED CITIZENS, AND THEN STACKING THEM INTO THIS MASSIVE THRONE OF FROZEN HUMAN AGONY.

67

MEANWHILE...

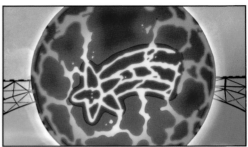

MABEL? MABEL!

OKAY, GUYS, BILL HAS TAKEN OVER THE TOWN, AND IF HIS WEIRDNESS SPREADS, HE'S GONNA TAKE OVER THE WHOLE WORLD.

OUR FIRST STEP TO STOPPING HIM IS RESCUING MABEL, BUT HE'S GOT HER TRAPPED IN THIS STRANGE PRISON BUBBLE.

WHAT IS THIS PLACE ANYWAY?

CRRACKLL

WHOA.

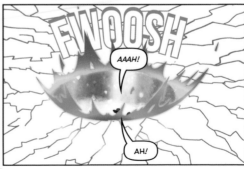

FWOOSH

AAAH!

AH!

70

"IT'S FUN O'CLOCK, EVERYONE.

"TODAY'S WEATHER CALLS FOR RAINBOWS WITH A CHANCE OF DANCE PARTIES.

"IF YOU ARE THE OWNER OF A UNICORN WITH A TOP HAT, PLEASE COME TO THE ICE-CREAM BEACH. YOUR UNICORN IS BEING TOWED."

WHAT IS THIS NEW WORLD? SHINING, SHIMMERING. SPLENDID!

KRPOE

WELCOME TO *MABELAND!*

"MABELAND!"

AND THIS IS WORSE THAN THE APOCALYPSE.

DUDE, THIS PLACE HURTS MY EYES.

OH, THAT'S NORMAL. MABELAND'S RAINBOWS HAVE COLORS ONLY BEES AND ART STUDENTS CAN SEE.

NOW, WHO WANTS TO GO ON THE GRAND TOUR?

DO WE HAVE A CHOICE?

NO!

73

MABELAND IS THE *ULTIMATE* PARADISE. AND THE ONLY RULE? THERE ARE *NO RULES!*

EXCEPT FOR ONE RULE, WHICH IS VERY SERIOUS—BUT NO ONE WOULD EVER BREAK IT, SO IT'S NOT WORTH MENTIONING!

YEAH!

LISTEN, CREEPY DREAM GUYS, WE'RE NOT HERE TO PARTY, OKAY?

WE JUST NEED TO FIND MABEL AND GET HER OUT OF HERE. WHERE IS SHE?

OUR HOMEGIRL, MABEL, LIVES AT OUR NEXT STOP.

WHOA!

NO RULES!

AND THAT GLITTER RAIN IS PROBABLY GROUND UP BONES OR BABIES OR SOMETHING.

BILL'S USING MABEL'S OWN FANTASIES AS SOME SICK TRAP. WE NEED TO GRAB MABEL AND GET THE HECK OUT OF HERE.

OH, MABEL? SHE'S AT THE TOP OF THE TALLEST TOWER GUARDED BY THOSE BIG, BUFF, WAFFLE GUARDS.

THERE'S NO WAY TO GET PAST *THEM.*

SOMEONE HAND ME SOME SYRUP.

77

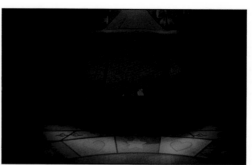

78

THE WAFFLES ARE COMING BACK! WE GOTTA HURRY!

UH, GUYS?

DON'T WORRY, MABEL, WE'LL GET YOU OUT OF THIS!

BUT, DIPPER...

CLAP CLAP

HEY!

WHAT THE—

OOF!

79

HYAH!

CLAP CLAP

MABEL, WHAT ARE YOU DOING?

WE'RE TRYING TO SAVE YOU FROM THIS PRISON!

THIS ISN'T A PRISON.

CLAP CLAP

I MADE THIS WORLD!

WELL, I SORT OF WOKE UP HERE. IT'S COMPLICATED.

WHAT ARE YOU SAYING?

MAYOR MABEL

I'M SAYING, THIS IS MY HOME NOW. AND I DON'T *WANNA* BE SAVED!

CLANG

SORRY, MABEL.

NO WORRIES, BUBBLE BEAR.

YOU DID *WHAT?*

LOOK, AFTER YOU SAID YOU WOULDN'T COME BACK HOME WITH ME AT THE END OF THE SUMMER FOR YOUR "APPRENTICESHIP," I WANTED TO HIDE IN MY SWEATER FOREVER.

BUT THEN I WOKE UP IN A PLACE THAT GIVES ME EXACTLY WHAT I WANTED--AN ENDLESS SUMMER WHERE WE'LL NEVER HAVE TO GROW UP!

HERE, THE SUN SHINES ALL DAY, THE PARTY NEVER ENDS, AND NOW THAT YOU GUYS ARE HERE, IT'S FINALLY *PERFECT.*

LISTEN, MABEL, WE'RE NOT HERE TO PARTY. ALL OF THIS IS CRAZY!

UGHH. I FIGURED *YOU* MIGHT SAY SOMETHING LIKE THAT, DIPPER.

THAT'S WHY I PREPARED A BACKUP DIPPER WITH A MORE SUPPORTIVE ATTITUDE.

WHOA!

UH!

YEAH!

WHAP

WIGGITY-WIGGITY WHAT'S UP, DUDE BROS? I'M DIPPY FRESH.

I LIKE SKATEBOARDING, SUPPORTING MY SISTER, AND PUNCTUATING EVERY SENTENCE WITH A HIGH FIVE.

HUP!

OH, DON'T MIND IF I--

:A-HEM:

I'M SORRY, I CAN'T LEAVE HIM HANGING.

YES!

YOU'RE DEAD TO ME, SOOS.

TRUST ME, YOU GUYS ARE GONNA *LOVE* IT HERE.

THIS WORLD ALWAYS KNOWS WHAT YOU WANT—SOMETIMES EVEN BEFORE YOU DO!

APPARENTLY, I WANTED A CHINCHILLA!

RIGHT AGAIN, MABELAND.

MABEL, LISTEN TO YOURSELF! THIS IS CRAZY! I'M SORRY ABOUT OUR FIGHT. AND I'M SORRY THINGS AREN'T GREAT RIGHT NOW, BUT THAT DOESN'T MEAN YOU CAN JUST STAY IN HERE FOREVER!

HEY, TAKE A CHILL PILL. THOSE GROW ON TREES HERE.

YOU STAY OUT OF THIS, DIPPY FRESH!

DUDE, CALM DOWN. DIPPY FRESH DIDN'T DO ANYTHING TO YOU, DAWG.

RRRNGH.

I KNOW IT SEEMS TOO GOOD TO BE TRUE, BUT JUST GIVE THIS PLACE A CHANCE.

CLAP CLAP

MABELAND KNOWS JUST WHAT YOU WANT AND ALWAYS PROVIDES.

:GASP:

:CHOMP: PUDDING CENTER. NICE.

ACTUALLY, MABEL, I'M WITH DIPPER ON THIS. GRAVITY FALLS IS IN TROUBLE, AND I REALLY THINK--

HONK HONK

NO RULEZ

WENDY!

WHA--GUYS? YOU'RE SAFE!

WE'VE GOT A MONSTER TRUCK FULL OF FIREWORKS, FAKE IDS, AND PRANKING SUPPLIES.

WANNA DRIVE THIS TRUCK THROUGH THE HIGH SCHOOL AND GLUE THIS PLUNGER TO THE PRINCIPAL'S HEAD?

YES. YES, I DO.

SORRY, GUYS, I'VE ALWAYS WANTED TO DO THAT. I'LL BE BACK IN JUST A FEW MINUTES.

WENDY?

WA-HOO!

DON'T WORRY, DUDE. THERE'S NOTHING IN THIS WORLD THAT COULD BREAK ME FROM OUR MISSION.

SOOS, MIJO. I HAVE RETURNED.

HOLY--WHOA, WHOA. DAD?

YOU DON'T REMEMBER WHAT I LOOK LIKE, SO I HAVE THE BODY OF A PRO WRESTLER AND A FACE YOU ONCE SAW ON A HOT-SAUCE BOTTLE.

I WAS NEVER THERE FOR YOU. BUT IN THIS WORLD, I CAN BE.

YOU'RE PERFECT!

IT'S A TRAP! DON'T GO WITH HIM, SOOS! NO MATTER WHAT HE OFFERS YOU.

WANT TO PLAY CATCH?

SORRY, DUDE. EVEN IF IT IS ALL A DREAM, I GOTTA PLAY JUST ONE GAME.

HA-HA. COME ON, DAD!

OKAY, THIS HAS GONE TOO FAR!

YOU CAN'T HONESTLY THINK THESE FANTASIES ARE GOOD FOR ANYONE?

YOU CAN'T ARGUE WITH THE RESULTS. PEOPLE ARE HAPPY HERE! DOES IT REALLY MATTER IF IT'S REAL OR NOT?

FOR ONCE, STOP LISTENING TO YOUR HEAD AND LISTEN TO YOUR HEART.

MABELAND HAS SOMETHING FOR EVERYONE. EVEN YOU! IN FACT--

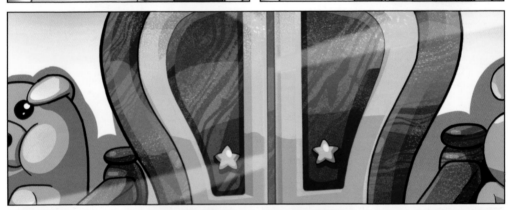

NOPE. NOT LOOKING. NOT LOOKING!

FEARAMID.

ALL RIGHT, CAN ANYBODY EXPLAIN TO ME WHY, EVEN WITH OUR NEWFOUND *INFINITE POWER...*

AAH!

...NONE OF US CAN ESCAPE THE BORDERS OF THIS STUPID HICK TOWN?

THERE'S SOME KIND OF FORCE FIELD KEEPING US IN. BUT WHO WOULD KNOW HOW TO FIX IT?

HMM, MAYBE *SOMEONE* NEEDS TO COME OUT OF RETIREMENT.

BILL!

UH, SORRY, BOSS, BUT GIDEON LET THE PINES FAMILY ESCAPE.

THEY'RE INSIDE MABEL'S BUBBLE AS WE SPEAK!

HA-HA-HA-HA-HA-HA! BUDDY, MABEL'S BUBBLE IS THE MOST DIABOLICAL TRAP I'VE EVER CREATED.

IT WOULD TAKE A WILL OF *TITANIUM* NOT TO GIVE INTO ITS TEMPTATION.

FETCH ME GIDEON AND TAKE THE REST OF THE DAY OFF. THINGS JUST GOT A LITTLE MORE INTERESTING.

MABELAND.

DUB-A-DUB-DUB. I'M A STUFFED ANIMAL TREE.

WE'RE STUFFED ANIMALS. TEE-HEE-HEE.

HAH!

FWIP

HA-HA-HA-HA!

AH-HA-HA-HA-HA.

GIGGLE CREEK

UGH! EVEN MY STONE SKIPS ARE PERFECT!

UGH, WHO AM I KIDDING? MAYBE MABEL'S RIGHT.

IT'S A HORROR SHOW OUT THERE.

AT LEAST THE AIR HERE IS BREATHABLE.

91

COME ON, MAN. JUST TAKE MY HAND.

WAIT! AAH, THIS ISN'T REAL!

AAAAUGHH! AH-AH-AH!

92

YOU SHOULDN'T HAVE DONE THAT, *DIPPER!* WE'RE WATCHING YOU.

THERE ARE EYES EVERYWHERE.

HEY, DIPPER!

HEY, DIPPER!

HEY, DIPPER!

HEY, DIPPER!

HEY, DIPPER!

DUB-A-DUB-DUB. I'M A STUFFED ANIMAL TREE.

AH. OH, MY GOSH. THIS IS CRAZY. I-I'M LOSING MY MIND. WE HAVE TO GET OUT OF HERE.

WE HAVE TO GO BACK... TO THE *REAL WORLD!*

94

MABEL, YOU'RE SMARTER THAN THIS!

BILL HAS YOU HYPNOTIZED OR SOMETHING! ARE YOU REALLY GONNA LET THEM *BANISH* ME?

NO! OF COURSE NOT. THAT'S MY BROTHER, GUYS. THERE'S GOTTA BE ANOTHER WAY.

VERY WELL. IF DIPPER WISHES TO STAY, HE MUST PLEAD HIS CASE IN THE ULTIMATE TRIAL OF FANTASY VERSUS REALITY.

:CHOMP:

HEY! SERIOUSLY?

MMM. IT WAS HIM.

COURTROOM.

AHHH.

SERIOUSLY, MABEL, YOU'RE LETTING THEM TAKE OUR ARGUMENT TO COURT?

HEY, I DIDN'T MAKE THE RULES IN MABELAND.

YES, YOU DID! THERE'S A TAPESTRY OF YOU MAKING THE RULES!

ALL RISE, FOR HONORABLE JUDGE KITTY-KITTY-MEOW-MEOW-FACE SHWARTZSTEIN.

97

IF DIPPER WINS, MABEL WILL RETURN WITH HIM TO THE REAL WORLD.

BUT IF HE LOSES, HE WILL BE BANISHED FOREVER AND REPLACED WITH TOWN DARLING DIPPY FRESH.

DIPPY, COME OUT.

FLIP-A-DIP-DIP!

I HATE HIM SO *MUCH!*

THE FINAL DECISION WILL BE MADE BY A JURY OF YOUR PEERS.

CLAP CLAP

HI, THERE. I LOVE YOUR HEADBAND.

SHUT YOUR MOUTH, I LOVE *YOUR* HEADBAND.

WE'RE ALL WEARING THE SAME HEADBAND!

WHOA! HA-HA! HEADBAND!

LOOK, MABEL, THIS WHOLE THING IS RIDICULOUS, BUT IF WINNING A TRIAL IS WHAT IT TAKES TO GET YOU TO COME HOME WITH US, THEN SO BE IT.

I'M SORRY, DIPPER, BUT I CAN ONLY SPEAK THROUGH MY LEGAL TEAM NOW.

WE HAVE A DOCTORATE DEGREE IN HUNKY-NESS.

ALSO, CRIMINAL AND INTERNATIONAL LAW.

LET'S HEAR OPENING STATEMENTS.

YOUR HONOR, TOWNSFOLK, LOVELY LADIES OF THE JURY--

OH, HE'S TALKING ABOUT US.

AHH! HA-HA-HA!

WE'RE NOT *THAT* LOVELY. OH.

MY CASE IS SIMPLE.

THIS VERY UNRIGHTEOUS DUDE THINKS THAT REALITY IS BETTER THAN FANTASY.

SECOND GRADE, OCTOBER TENTH...

PHOTO DAY.

:SNIFF: DARN ALLERGIES.

BOOM!

A MILLION SLAP BRACELETS! I'M GONNA HAVE THE BEST PHOTO *EVER!*

AND HOW DO YOU LIKE MY NEW PIGTAILS?

102

MABEL'S FANTASY WAS HAVING A GREAT SCHOOL PHOTO, BUT REALITY HAD OTHER PLANS.

LOOK, THAT WAS *ONE* BAD DAY.

ONE OF MANY. FEBRUARY FOURTEENTH, FOURTH GRADE. VALENTINE'S DAY...

OH, COME ON, MAN, YOU CAN'T.

HOW MANY VALENTINES DID *YOU* GET, DIPPER?

OH, HEY. HEH-HEH. DIPPER DIDN'T GET ANY! OH, MAN, I THOUGHT I WAS THE CLASS LOSER.

HEY, EVERYONE! DIPSTICK DIDN'T GET ANY!

HA-HA-HA-HA! DIPSTICK! DIPSTICK!

UGH. -:SOB:-

I CAN'T BELIEVE THAT KID'S YOUR BROTHER.

HEY, WHAT'S THE POINT OF ALL THIS? THAT WAS IN THE PAST!

IS YOUR LIFE ANY BETTER NOW, BRO?

BAD MEMORIES

HEARTBREAK...

...DISASTER...

...BROKEN PROMISES. THAT'S REALITY FOR YOU.

OUT THERE, IT'S NOTHING BUT HEARTBREAK. BUT IN HERE? WHO WANTS PUG SUNDAES?

AHH...

HAND ME A MICROPHONE, XYLER.

TOTALLY RIGHTEOUS, BRO.

ARE WE *BROTHERS?*

I DON'T KNOW!

WELL, I THINK WE'RE READY FOR A VERDICT.

WAIT! I HAVEN'T EVEN PRESENTED MY CASE!

HEH-HEH!

DO YOU EVEN HAVE A CASE?

YES, I DO, YOUR HONOR. I CALL AS A WITNESS, MABEL PINES.

÷GASP÷

UH... OBJECTION?

I'LL ALLOW IT. US CATS ARE FAMOUSLY CURIOUS. MEOW, MEOW.

OH, MY! THIS IS SO...

:SIGH: MABEL, LISTEN, I MIGHT NOT HAVE ALL THE ANSWERS.

I'M NOT STYLISH, AND I'M NOT COOL, AND I CAN'T MAKE PUGS APPEAR OUT OF THIN AIR.

COME ON!

WHAT?

BOO! GUILTY!

BOO!

BUT I KNOW ONE THING WELL, AND THAT'S YOU.

AND I KNOW THAT EVEN THOUGH YOU MIGHT ACT LIKE IT, YOU DON'T WANT TO BE IN THIS FANTASY WORLD.

UH...-PFFT- YEAH, RIGHT.

YOU'RE SCARED OF GROWING UP.

AND WHO COULD BLAME YOU? I'M SCARED TOO.

MEOW

UH, LA-LA-LA-LA-LA-LA, I'M NOT LISTENING!

GUARDS! THE FINGERS!

CLAP CLAP

MEOW

LOOK, REAL LIFE STINKS SOMETIMES, OKAY? I'M NOT GONNA LIE.

BUT THERE'S A BETTER WAY TO GET THROUGH IT THAN DENIAL, AND THAT'S WITH HELP FROM PEOPLE WHO CARE ABOUT YOU.

IT'S HOW WE'VE GOTTEN THROUGH OUR WHOLE LIVES. JUST LOOK.

WE'VE *ALWAYS* BEEN THERE FOR EACH OTHER.

MABEL, I THOUGHT YOU WERE LIVING A FANTASY, BUT LOOK AT ME! I ACTUALLY THOUGHT I WAS GONNA STAY HERE AND BE FORD'S APPRENTICE.

SPEND MY ENTIRE TEENS COOPED UP IN A BASEMENT WITH A LAB COAT? HOW RIDICULOUS IS THAT?

I DON'T KNOW WHAT'S GONNA HAPPEN IN THE FUTURE, BUT WHATEVER IT IS, YOU DON'T HAVE TO FEAR, BECAUSE WE'LL DO IT TOGETHER.

I'M *NOT* TAKING FORD'S APPRENTICESHIP. WE'VE TRAVELED TO HECK AND BACK TO GET YOU, AND WE'RE GOING BACK TOGETHER.

DON'T DO THE PATS!

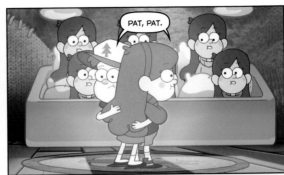

PAT, PAT.

PWUFF

OH, MAN. I NEVER NOTICED HOW *BRIGHT* THIS PLACE IS.

UGH, HAVE I ACTUALLY BEEN LISTENING TO THE SAME SONG FOR AN ENTIRE WEEK?

MROWR!

WHOA! TIME TO CALM YOU DOWN.

CLAP CLAP

UH, WHY ISN'T THIS WORKING?

CLAP CLAP

115

WHOA. YOU ALL GOOD? EVERYONE GOOD?

HA-HA-HA-HA!

WE'VE MISSED YOU, MABEL.

OINK

HEY, DIPPER, I APPRECIATE WHAT YOU SAID BACK THERE, BUT IF YOU WANNA TAKE FORD'S APPRENTICESHIP, I WON'T GET IN YOUR WAY.

:PFFT: MISS OUT ON YOUR AWKWARD TEEN YEARS? YOU WISH. HA-HA.

HA-HA-HA! MAN, I WENT NUTS BACK THERE.

I MEAN, COME ON, THE REAL WORLD CAN'T BE *THAT* BAD, RIGHT?

OH, BOY.

WHERE IS EVERYONE?

THE TOWN'S DESERTED.

DID BILL ALREADY WIN?

COME ON, GUYS. LET'S SEE IF WE CAN GO HIDE OUT IN THE SHACK.

YES! IT'S IN SHAMBLES! JUST LIKE WE LEFT IT.

OH, MAN, THIS IS THE FIRST TIME I'VE EVER FELT HAPPY GOING TO WORK.

HELLO, HOUSE. HELLO, PORCH. HELLO, WADS OF GUM I LEFT STUCK TO THE COUCH!

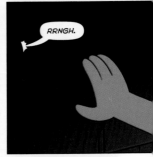

RRNGH.

WAIT, WHAT WAS THAT? SSHH.

LET'S GET 'EM, DUDES.

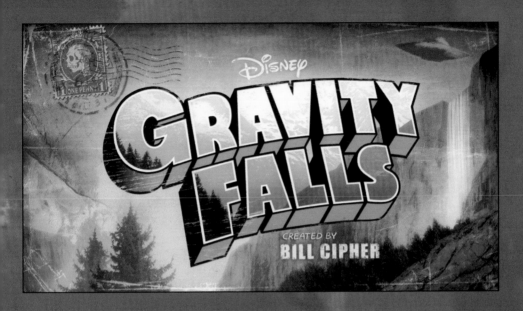

WEIRDMAGEDDON 3:
TAKE BACK THE FALLS

WAIT...

MYSTERY SHACK.

GRUNKLE STAN!

KIDS! I CAN'T BELIEVE IT...I THOUGHT I LOST YOU TWO.

AGH!

MR. PINES, IT'S REALLY YOU! I'VE BEEN HUGGING STRANGERS TO PRACTICE FOR THIS MOMENT.

WE MISSED YOU, YOU OLD CODGER!

HAH-HAH. I'VE MISSED YOU KNUCKLEHEADS TOO. IT'S GOOD TO HAVE YOU BACK.

121

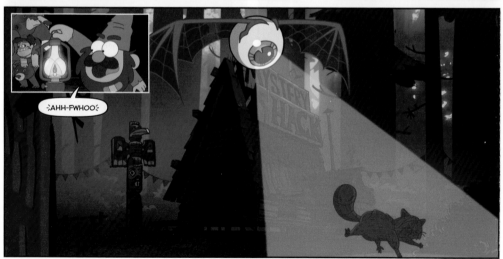

123

124

"WHAT I DIDN'T EXPECT WAS WHAT HAPPENED NEXT.

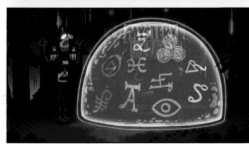

"TURNS OUT WHATEVER YOU AND MY BROTHER DID TO THE SHACK WITH YOUR UNICORN VOODOO MADE THE CRAZY PLACE INVINCIBLE TO WEIRDNESS."

OF *COURSE*. THE UNICORN SPELL! THAT'S WHY THIS IS THE ONLY PLACE BILL'S MAGIC CAN'T TOUCH.

THAT'S WHEN POSSUM BREATH OVER HERE SHOWS UP LEADING A BUNCH OF INJURED STRAGGLERS THROUGH THE FOREST.

THEY NEEDED A PLACE TO STAY, AND SINCE THE MAYOR GOT CAPTURED, I ELECTED MYSELF DE FACTO CHIEF.

THE PLAN'S TO STAY IN HERE AND EAT BROWN MEAT UNTIL WE RUN OUT.

THEN I VOTE WE EAT THE GNOMES.

HEY, I'M SHORT, NOT DEAF!

SHH, SHH! STRESS WILL MAKE YOU CHEWY.

GRUNKLE STAN, WE CAN'T ALL JUST HIDE INSIDE THE SHACK. THERE'S A TOWN IN NEED OF *SAVING*.

ME AND FORD TRIED TO DO IT, BUT HE GOT CAPTURED BY BILL.

SERVES THAT JERK RIGHT! MY BROTHER'S HAD SOME STUPID PLANS, BUT GOING UP AGAINST AN ALL-POWERFUL SPACE DEMON WAS HIS WORST ONE YET.

TRUST ME, WE HAVE EVERYTHING WE NEED RIGHT HERE!

IT'S NOT THE RITZ, BUT AT LEAST THE MONSTERS *INSIDE* KNOW HOW TO MASSAGE.

YOU KNOW SHIATSU?

YES, I'VE TAKEN SOME CLASSES.

SO YOU'RE REALLY JUST GONNA LET BILL WIN?

LOOK, KIDDO, WE GOT A GOOD DEAL HERE. BESIDES, I'M SURE WHEREVER THE REST OF THE TOWNSFOLK ARE, THEY'RE *FINE*.

CLICK

THIS IS SHANDRA JIMENEZ, REPORTING LIVE FROM THE INSIDE OF BILL'S CASTLE.

HERE FOR THE FIRST TIME ARE IMAGES OF WHAT'S HAPPENED TO THE CAPTURED TOWNSFOLK.

CHAIR-IBLE FATE!

VIEWERS ARE ADVISED TO LOOK AWAY IF THEY DON'T WANT TO SEE THEIR FRIENDS TURNED INTO A TWISTED THRONE OF HUMAN AGONY.

CHAIR-IBLE FATE!

CHAIR-IBLE FATE!

CHAIR-IBLE FATE!

CHAIR-IBLE FATE!

MOM AND DAD?

MY FAMILY!

DEPUTY DURLAND!

128

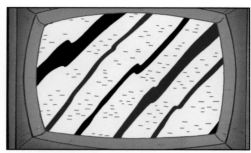

IS THERE **NO ONE** WHO WILL SAVE THE PEOPLE OF THIS TOWN? I'M SHANDRA JIMENEZ, AND I'M BEING TURNED INTO STONE BY A FLYING EYEBALL.

GASP

OH, NO. MY PARENTS ARE BAD, BUT EVEN **THEY** DON'T DESERVE TO BE TURNED TO **STONE.**

CURSE YOU, BILL!

WHY MUST YOU TAKE EVERYTHING WE LOVE? SOB

GUYS, DON'T YOU SEE? OUR FRIENDS NEED US, BUT WE CAN ONLY SAVE THEM IF WE **FIGHT BACK!**

MABEL IS RIGHT. BILL WANTS US TO RUN AND HIDE...

...HE WANTS US TO THINK HE'S INVINCIBLE, BUT FORD TOLD ME BEFORE HE WAS CAPTURED THAT HE KNOWS BILL'S SECRET WEAKNESS.

:GASP:

SECRET?

SECRET WEAKNESS?

NOW, IF WE BAND TOGETHER...

...IF WE COMBINE ALL OF OUR STRENGTHS...

...OUR SMARTS...

...OUR... WHATEVER TOBY HAS...

HAIRIEST RASHES!

130

...THEN WE JUST MIGHT BE ABLE TO RESCUE FORD, LEARN BILL'S WEAKNESS, AND SAVE *GRAVITY FALLS!*

YEAH!

YEAH!

WA-HOO!

WHOA, WHOA, WHOA. HAVE YOU ALL FORGOTTEN WHO'S IN CHARGE HERE? BESIDES, WE'RE ONLY SAFE INSIDE.

IT'S NOT LIKE WE CAN TAKE THE MYSTERY SHACK TO BILL.

WUH-WHOO! HOLY HOOTENANNY! FLAPJACK AND FIDDLEBANJOS!

SORRY, SORRY, GOT A LITTLE EXCITED.

FEARAMID.

LET ME GO, YOU INSANE THREE-SIDED... WH-WHAT IS THIS PLACE?

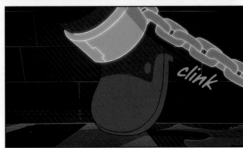

clink

133

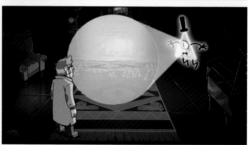

136

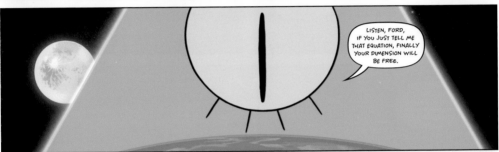

137

I'LL REMAKE A FUN WORLD, A BETTER WORLD.

A PARTY THAT NEVER ENDS, WITH A HOST THAT NEVER DIES—NO MORE RESTRICTIONS, NO MORE LAWS!

YOU'D BE ONE OF US. ALL POWERFUL, GREATER THAN ANYTHING YOU'VE IMAGINED.

AND ALL I NEED IS YOUR HELP.

YOU'RE INSANE IF YOU THINK I'LL HELP YOU.

HA-HA-HA! I'M INSANE EITHER WAY, BRAINIAC, BUT HAVE IT YOUR WAY!

ALL RIGHT, I'VE MADE SOME THINGAMADICULOUS ROBOMAGIGS IN MY DAY, BUT THIS IS THE FIRST ONE THAT WON'T BE USED FOR EVIL.

WHOA! THESE BLUEPRINTS ARE *INCREDIBLE,* MCGUCKET.

THIS IS YOUR MOST AMAZING INVENTION YET!

QUESTION-- DOES IT HAVE ANY GUN- SWORDS?

I WATCH A LOT OF ANIME, AND--*HEH*--TRUST ME, YOU'RE GONNA WANT SOME GUN- SWORDS.

WHAT'S AN ANIME?

WE HAVE MUCH TO DISCUSS.

DISCUSS NOTHING, THESE SCRIBBLES ARE A BUNCH OF COCKAMAMY BALDERDASH. EXCUSE MY FRENCH.

‹JE NE SAIS QUOI SACRE BLUE AU REVOIR.›*

*I DON'T BELIEVE THAT WAS FRENCH.

WHERE WOULD YOU EVEN FIND A BUNCH OF IDIOTS CRAZY ENOUGH TO BUILD IT?

GRUNKLE STAN, YOU'RE *LOOKING* AT THOSE IDIOTS.

WOO! YEAH! HA-HA!

IDIOTS!

GRAVITY FALLS

142

LATER...

THANKS FOR THESE APOCALYPSE SWEATERS, MABEL, THE END OF THE WORLD HAS NEVER BEEN SO *COMFORTABLE.*

MM-HM!

BRRR.

AH, FINE, I'LL WEAR IT. BUT I'M NOT GONNA LIKE IT.

144

ADMIT IT, THIS IS THE BEST DAY OF THE END OF THE WORLD—I THINK WE ACTUALLY HAVE A CHANCE TO BEAT BILL AND WIN BACK OUR FUTURE.

YEAH, GETTING TO ACTUALLY *LIVE* TO SEE OUR THIRTEENTH BIRTHDAY PARTY IS THE ONLY BIRTHDAY PRESENT I WANT RIGHT NOW.

HEY, IF WE'RE LUCKY ENOUGH TO GET THERE, I GUARANTEE THIS WHOLE TOWN IS GONNA THROW YOU THE BEST BIRTHDAY PARTY YOU'VE EVER SEEN.

THANKS, SOOS. HEY, HAS ANYONE SEEN GRUNKLE STAN?

THIS WHOLE PLAN IS *BONKERS*. OF COURSE, NO ONE ASKED THE CHIEF WHAT HE THINKS.

AFTER ALL I'VE DONE FOR EVERYONE.

SHMEBULOCK.

YEAH, EXACTLY. IT'S A TOTAL LOAD OF SHMEBULOCK.

IS SOMETHING WRONG, GRUNKLE STAN? YOU'RE ACTING...GRUNKLIER THAN USUAL.

145

IT'S THIS DARN PLAN TO SAVE MY BROTHER.

IF YOU DIDN'T NOTICE, I ALREADY SAVED HIM ONCE FROM THAT PORTAL, AND HE NEVER THANKED ME.

OBJECTIVE: SAVE FORD!

HE CAUSES THE END OF THE WORLD, AND SOMEHOW IT'S STILL ALWAYS "STAN'S THE SCREWUP," "FORD'S THE HERO."

OBJECTIVE: SAVE FORD!

WELL, MAYBE PEOPLE THINK HE'S A HERO BECAUSE HE DIDN'T WANNA HIDE IN THE MYSTERY SHACK.

WELL, MAYBE IF HE HID IN THE MYSTERY SHACK HE WOULDN'T HAVE BEEN CAPTURED!

OBJECTIVE: SAVE F...

GUYS! GUYS! TRUST ME, TOMORROW'S GONNA BE GREAT. I BELIEVE IN US.

HELP, LEADER MABEL! I KEEP ACCIDENTALLY FLEXING THROUGH MY SWEATER. UGH! IT HAPPENED AGAIN.

THOSE WEIRD COW-MONSTERS ARE DELIGHTFUL.

COMING!

CHIEF

CHIEF

146

LATER...

ALL RIGHT, FELLAS. LET'S HOPE THIS TURNS OUT BETTER THAN MY OTHER INVENTIONS.

EVERYBODY, READY? DIPPER, NOW!

URGH!

CLANK

WHOA! WHOA!

NO! NO, NO!

AH-HA-HA-HA!

FEARAMID.

AAAGHH!

READY TO TALK NOW?

⌐SIGH⌐ I WON'T--I WON'T LET YOU INTO MY MIND.

WHAT DO YOU THINK, PALS? ANOTHER FIVE HUNDRED VOLTS? HEY, DO YOU HEAR THAT?

RRRRRRRuuuuuuuUMN MMM MMM MBBBBBBBBBILLLLLLEEEE

RAAAUGGGHHHH

WHAT? I JUST FIXED THAT DOOR.

149

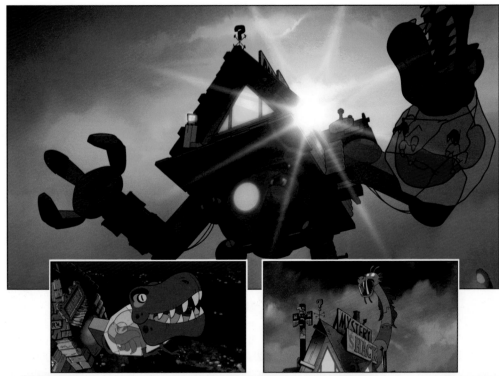

IT'S THE *SHACKTRON*, DUDE!

THEY MADE THE HOUSE INTO A ROBOT. FASCINATING!

OH, HEY DUDES. IS THIS THING ON? TEST.

HEH. UH, I JUST WANTED YOU MONSTER DUDES TO HAND OVER FORD OR WE'LL HAVE TO, LIKE, FIGHT AND JUNK.

HEH-HEH. HEY, YOU'RE A LITTLE CUTIE.

I HAVE BUTCHERED *MILLIONS* ON COUNTLESS MOONS.

WHOA! I LIKED YOU BETTER BEFORE YOU TALKED. REAL, REAL, BRING DOWN THIS GUY.

ATTACK!

EVERYONE, LIKE WE PLANNED! THREE, TWO, ONE, GO!

RAAGHHHH!

OINK OINK

HA-HA-HA! GOOD PIG.

GET 'EM, GOBBLEWONKER! WOO-HOO-HA-HA-HA-HA!

HYAH!

154

AAAAAAAAAAAH!

GUYS, SERIOUSLY? YOU HAD, LIKE, ONE JOB TO DO HERE.

BRAVO, DIPPER AND MABEL!

WELL, WOULD YOU LOOK AT THAT. THOSE KIDS REALLY CARE ABOUT YOU.

AND YOU CARE ABOUT THEM, *DON'T YOU?*

WHAT ARE YOU...OH... OH, NO!

PERHAPS TORTURING THOSE KIDS'LL MAKE YOU TALK.

NO, NO! NOT THE KIDS, YOU CA--

LET'S GET THIS OVER WITH.

CRRRCK

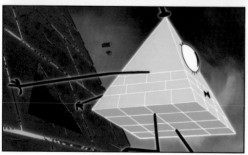

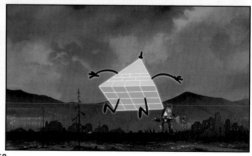

THCCCOM

VORP

WHAT THE--NO!
NO, NO, NO,
NO!

WE'VE GOT HIM DISTRACTED! NOW'S OUR CHANCE!

RESCUE TEAM! MOVE OUT!

UWSSH

MYSTERY SHACK

CRASH

OKAY, EVERYONE-- WE GET IN, RESCUE FORD, GET OUT, SAVE THE WORLD. PIECE OF CAKE.

JUST SO WE'RE CLEAR, IF I DIE, I'M SUING ALL OF YOU.

HEY, ON SECOND THOUGHT, MAYBE WE COULD COME UP WITH A PLAN THAT DOESN'T INVOLVE US PLUMMETING TO OUR CERTAIN DEATH--

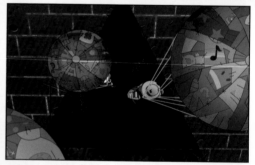

GASP

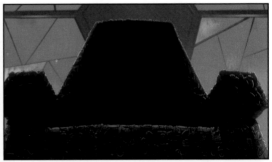

MAN, IT LOOKS EVEN WORSE UP CLOSE.

CLANK

SHOOOOOOSH

I'VE GOT GREAT UNCLE FORD! HE'S GOLDEN--BUT NOT IN THE GOOD WAY.

GREAT! GRAB HIM AND LET'S GET OUTTA HERE.

BUT HOW ARE WE GOING TO UNFREEZE THEM?

163

I KNOW!

EH-EH-EH-EH.

GIDEON, WHAT *HAPPENED* TO YOU?

BILL CAPTURED ME. HE'S BEEN FORCING ME TO DO CUTE DANCES IN THIS CAGE FOR ALL ETERNITY. AH-HA-HA.

I'M SO TIRED OF BEING CUTE. -:SOB:-

HOW DO WE UNDO THIS?

MAYOR TYLER. HE'S THE LOAD-BEARING HUMAN. PULL HIM OUT AND THE WHOLE THING GOES DOWN.

MM-UGH!

165

KIDS! AH, YOU DID IT! I KNEW I COULD COUNT ON YOU TWO. HAH-HAH!

FIDDLEFORD... I-I HAVEN'T SEEN YOU SINCE WE PARTED WAYS.

YOU MUST HATE ME.

I'VE TRIED FORGETTIN'. MAYBE I SHOULD TRY FORGIVIN'. COME HERE, OLD FRIEND.

HEY, GOOD TO SEE YOU, TOO, BRO. NOW LET'S GET OUT OF HERE, HUH?

LISTEN, UNCLE FORD. WE DON'T HAVE A LOT OF TIME.

REMEMBER HOW YOU TOLD ME, RIGHT BEFORE YOU WERE FROZEN, THAT YOU KNEW BILL'S WEAKNESS?

YEAH, A SECRET WAY TO DEFEAT HIM?

I-I DO. NOW, DOES ANYONE HAVE A PEN? PENCIL? ANYTHING?

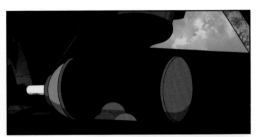

AH. PERFECT!

AH...WE'VE GOT BILL OUTSIDE, BUT I DON'T KNOW HOW LONG WE CAN KEEP HIM OCCUPIED.

YES, YES. GOOD, GOOD.

DRAWING A CIRCLE ON THE FLOOR. WELL, HE'S LOST HIS MIND.

MY MIND IS FINE. AND THERE IS A WAY TO BEAT HIM. WITH THIS!

THE WORLD'S MOST CONFUSING GAME OF HOPSCOTCH?

NO--A PROPHECY... ALTHOUGH, IT WOULD BE A PRETTY FUN GAME OF HOPSCOTCH.

"MANY YEARS AGO, I FOUND TEN SYMBOLS IN A CAVE. SOME I RECOGNIZED THEN, SOME I ONLY RECOGNIZE NOW.

"THE NATIVE PEOPLE OF GRAVITY FALLS PROPHESIZED THAT THESE SYMBOLS COULD CREATE A FORCE STRONG ENOUGH TO VANQUISH BILL.

"WITH BILL DEFEATED, HIS WEIRDNESS WOULD BE REVERSED AND THE TOWN COULD BE SAVED."

THIS WHOLE TIME, I THOUGHT IT WAS JUST SUPERSTITION, BUT SEEING YOU ALL HERE NOW, I FINALLY UNDERSTAND THAT IT'S *DESTINY*.

DIPPER, THE PINE TREE.

MABEL, THE SHOOTING STAR.

THE QUESTION MARK! THIS ONE'S UNSOLVABLE.

THAT ONE'S *EASY!* YOU'VE BEEN ROCKING THAT DUMB HOODIE SINCE THE SEVENTH GRADE!

WHOA... DESTINY HOODIE.

THE TENT OF TELEPATHY SIGN! THAT MUST BE GIDEON.

WOO! AN EXCUSE TO STAND NEXT TO MABEL!

DON'T TURN THIS INTO A BIG DEAL.

OH, I WON'T.

I WILL!

169

FEARAMID.

HOLD HANDS, EVERYONE. THIS IS A MYSTICAL HUMAN ENERGY CIRCUIT.

ICE? WHO'S ICE?

THE SYMBOLS NEEDN'T ALL BE LITERAL, DIPPER.

IT JUST HAS TO BE SOMEONE COOL IN THE FACE OF DANGER.

WENDY! WENDY!

HA-HA. SHUT UP, YOU GUYS.

MUCH LIKE THE SPECTACLES NEED TO BE SOMEONE SCHOLARLY.

HEH-HEH!

THIS IS FREAKY.

NOW, HOLD HANDS, EVERYONE!

EW! I'M NOT TOUCHING THAT.

DO IT, SWEETIE. DO THE ONE THING NO ONE IN OUR FAMILY HAS EVER DONE.

TOUCH THE HILLBILLY.

:GASP:

GREAT UNCLE FORD, I THINK IT'S *WORKING!*

OOH, OOH! HEH-HEH-HAH-HAH-HAH!

YES! THIS IS IT.

THE REST OF YOU, GET OUT! IT'S TOO DANGEROUS.

WE JUST NEED ONE MORE PERSON. STANLEY! *STANLEY,* GET OVER HERE.

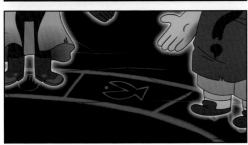

YOU'RE THE ONLY ONE LEFT!

I SPENT *THIRTY YEARS* TRYING TO BRING YOU BACK INTO THIS DIMENSION AND YOU *STILL* HAVEN'T THANKED ME!

YOU WANT ME TO SHAKE YOUR HAND? SAY "THANK YOU."

FINE. THANK YOU.

AH, SEE? BETWEEN ME AND HIM, I'M NOT ALWAYS THE BAD TWIN.

BETWEEN HIM AND ME. GRAMMAR, STANLEY.

I'LL GRAMMAR STANLEY YOU! *YOU* STUCK-UP SON OF A GUN.

DON'T JEOPARDIZE THIS, YOU IDIOT! EVERYTHING'S ON THE LINE!

GUYS, STOP IT! JUST HUG IT OUT! NOW IS NOT THE TIME.

JOIN HANDS!

176

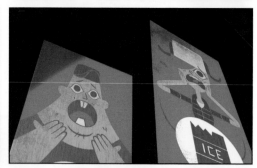

179

180

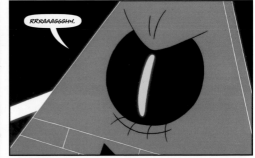

181

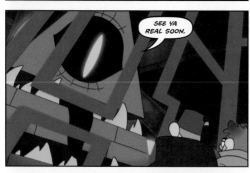

182

THE KIDS ARE GONNA DIE AND IT'S ALL MY FAULT BECAUSE I COULDN'T SHAKE YOUR STUPID HAND.

AH, DAD WAS RIGHT ABOUT ME.

I *AM* A SCREWUP.

AAH, DON'T BLAME YOURSELF.

I'M THE ONE WHO MADE A DEAL WITH BILL IN THE FIRST PLACE. I FELL FOR ALL HIS EASY FLATTERY.

YOU WOULD HAVE SEEN HIM FOR THE SCAM ARTIST HE IS.

HOW DID THINGS GET SO MESSED UP BETWEEN US?

WE USED TO BE LIKE DIPPER AND MABEL.

WORLD'S ABOUT TO END AND THEY *STILL* WORK TOGETHER. HOW DO THEY DO IT?

EASY, THEY'RE KIDS--THEY DON'T KNOW ANY BETTER.

WHOA, WHERE ARE YOU GOING?

I'M GONNA PLAY THE ONLY CARD WE HAVE LEFT--LET BILL INTO MY MIND.

HE'LL BE ABLE TO TAKE OVER THE GALAXY AND MAYBE EVEN WORSE. BUT AT LEAST HE *MIGHT* LET THE KIDS FREE.

WHAT? ARE YOU KIDDING ME? ARE YOU HONESTLY TELLING ME THERE'S NOTHING ELSE WE CAN DO?

BILL'S ONLY WEAK IN THE MIND-SPACE.

IF I DIDN'T HAVE THIS DARN PLATE IN MY HEAD WE COULD JUST ERASE HIM WITH THE MEMORY GUN WHEN HE STEPS INSIDE MY MIND.

WHAT IF HE GOES INTO *MY* MIND? MY BRAIN ISN'T GOOD FOR ANYTHING.

HEH-HEH. THERE'S NOTHING IN YOUR MIND HE WANTS.

IT *HAS* TO BE ME. WE NEED TO TAKE HIS DEAL.

IT'S THE ONLY WAY HE'LL AGREE TO SAVE YOU AND THE KIDS.

DO YOU REALLY THINK HE'S GONNA MAKE GOOD ON THAT DEAL?

WHAT OTHER CHOICE DO WE HAVE?

185

ELSEWHERE...

PANT
AH!

YOU KNOW, I'M STARTING TO THINK THERE'S NO WAY OUT OF HERE.

LIKE GRUNKLE STAN ALWAYS SAYS, "WHEN ONE DOOR CLOSES, CHOOSE A NEARBY WALL AND BASH IT IN WITH BRUTE FORCE!"

UGH. AAGH!

SHWU

AAAAHHHHHHH!

KRRRRSH

HAH! NOW, LET'S ROUND UP THE TOWNSFOLK AND TOGETHER WE CAN DEFEAT--

--OH, NO.

187

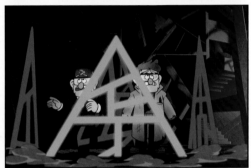

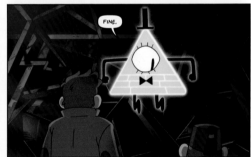

189

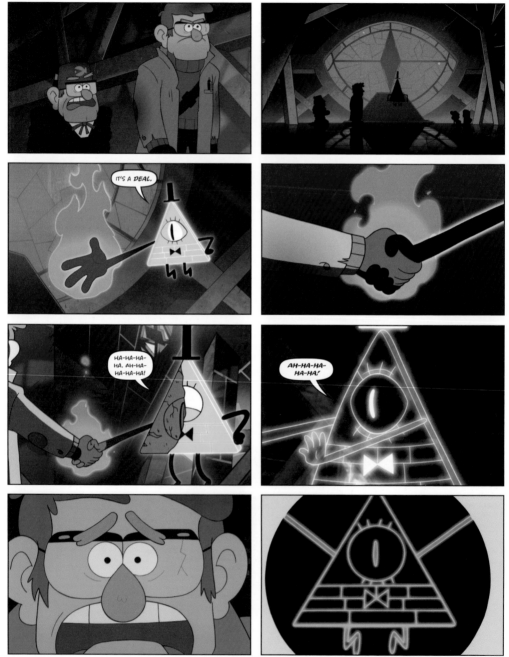

190

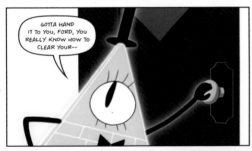

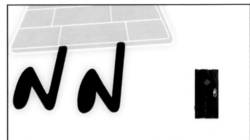

191

Y-YOU IDIOT, DON'T YOU REALIZE YOU'RE DESTROYING YOUR OWN MIND TOO?

EH, IT'S NOT LIKE I WAS USIN' THIS SPACE FOR MUCH ANYWAY.

LET ME OUT OF HERE! LET ME OUT!

WHY ISN'T THIS WORKING?

HEY, LOOK AT ME.

TURN AROUND AND LOOK AT ME, YOU ONE-EYED DEMON!

YOU'RE A REAL WISE GUY, BUT YOU MADE ONE FATAL MISTAKE. YOU MESSED WITH MY FAMILY.

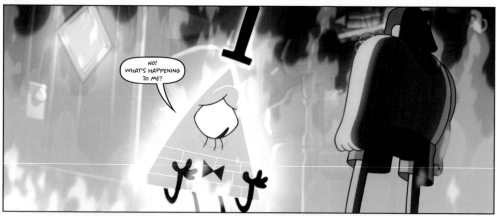

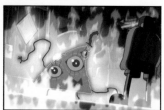

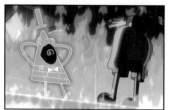

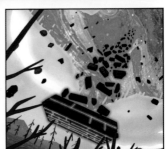

OH, MY GOSH, GRUNKLE STAN, YOU *DID IT!*

OH, UH, HEY THERE... KIDDO. WHAT'S YOUR NAME?

HAH... GRUNKLE STAN?

HEH. WHO YOU TALKIN' TO?

C-COME ON, IT'S ME. IT'S ME, GRUNKLE STAN!

GRUNKLE STAN! IT'S ME!

WE HAD TO ERASE HIS MIND TO DEFEAT BILL. IT'S ALL GONE.

STAN HAS NO IDEA, BUT HE DID IT--HE SAVED THE WORLD.

HE SAVED THE WORLD, BUT WHAT'S THE POINT? GRUNKLE STAN'S NOT HIMSELF ANYMORE.

THERE'S GOTTA BE *SOMETHING* WE CAN DO TO JOG HIS MEMORY.

THERE ISN'T. I'M SORRY, STAN'S GONE.

I *KNOW* MY GRUNKLE IS IN THERE SOMEWHERE.

THERE'S GOTTA BE SOMETHING AROUND HERE THAT CAN HELP BRING HIM BACK.

THIS'LL WORK! THIS HAS TO WORK.

HERE'S THE FIRST DAY WE CAME TO GRAVITY FALLS, GRUNKLE STAN.

DAY 1

MYSTERY

AND HERE'S A MACARONI INTERPRETATION OF MY EMOTIONS.

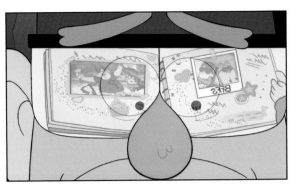

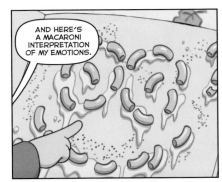

THAT TIME WE WENT FISHING? THAT SUMMERWEEN WE SPENT TOGETHER. DON'T YOU REMEMBER ANYTHING?

I'M SORRY, I DON'T KNOW WHAT THIS IS, OR WHO YOU ARE--

OINK

GAH! QUIT IT, WADDLES!

I'M TRYING TO REMEMBER MY LIFE STORY!

GASP

WHAT DID YOU SAY?

I SAID, GET WADDLES OFF OF ME!

204

"GOOD MORNING, GRAVITY FALLS. IT'S ANOTHER BEAUTIFUL DAY, BUT EVERY DAY IS BEAUTIFUL NOW THAT THE...UNPLEASANTNESS IS OVER."

GET OUT OF HERE, YOU ORNERY CRITTERS.

205

RAAUGGHHHH.

SPLORCH

AH, GOOD AS NEW.

OH, LOOKS LIKE YOU'VE GOT A FRIEND!

ROBBIE, WOULD YOU BE A DEAR AND GET US THE SAWED-OFF SHOTGUN?

UGH. FINE. WHATEVER.

BRAINS AND SO FORTH!

NOPE. NONE OF THAT, THANK YOU.

splorch

HA-HA-HA-HA-HA!

...TO YOU!

WA-HOO! YEAH! WOO!

I CAN'T BELIEVE YOU ALL GOT TOGETHER JUST TO THROW A PARTY FOR *US.*

AFTER ALL THE PINES FAMILY HAS DONE FOR THE TOWN, IT'S THE LEAST WE COULD DO!

YOU'VE HELPED EVERYONE HERE.

THANKS TO Y'ALL SAVIN' US, I LEARNED TO OPEN MY HEART TO KINDNESS.

NO MORE EVIL DOIN'! FROM NOW ON, I'M GONNA TRY TO BE LI'L GIDEON, REGULAR OL' KID.

OH! AH-HAH-HA.

WOO!

HEH, I'M BUSTIN' A MOVE ON THIS SKATIN' BOARD.

MORE LIKE BUSTING YOUR PANTS, LOSER. HEH-HEH-HEH-HEH.

SNAP

WAAAHHHHH!

HE-HE-HE.

210

DUDE, MAKE A WISH, DAWG!

YOU KNOW, ON MY FIRST DAY HERE, IF YOU HAD ASKED ME WHAT I WANTED...

...I WOULD HAVE SAID ADVENTURE, MYSTERY, TRUE FRIENDS...

...BUT LOOKING HERE AT ALL OF YOU, I REALIZE THAT EVERY WISH CAME TRUE.

I HAVE EVERYTHING I WANTED.

IF I HAD ONLY ONE WISH, IT WOULD BE TO SHRINK ALL OF YOU WITH THE SHRINK RAY AND BRING YOU HOME WITH US IN MY POCKET.

BUT SINCE THAT'S IMPOSSIBLE...IS THAT IMPOSSIBLE?

...SINCE THAT'S PROBABLY IMPOSSIBLE, MY ONLY WISH IS FOR EVERYONE TO SIGN MY SCRAPBOOK.

I'LL NEVER FORGET YOU GUYS. WAIT.

URGH.

KRRRSH

NOW I'LL NEVER FORGET YOU GUYS.

-FWHOO-

I NOW OFFICIALLY DECLARE YOU TECHNICALLY TEENAGERS! WELCOME TO ANGST AND ACNE FOREVER.

ONE OF US! ONE OF US!

WA-HOO!

YAY!

COOL

SO, HOW DO YOU FEEL?

SAME-Y. BUT DIFFERENT-Y.

HEY, YOU TWO! WHEN ARE YOU GONNA OPEN YOUR PRESENTS ALREADY? I BROKE A NAIL WRAPPING THEM.

HA-HA-HA. PACIFICA.

STANLEY, I NEED TO TALK TO YOU.

I DIDN'T WANNA SAY ANYTHING WITH EVERYBODY LISTENING, BUT WE'VE GOT A PROBLEM.

WEIRDMAGEDDON HAS BEEN CONTAINED, BUT I'M DETECTING SOME STRANGE NEW ANOMALIES NEAR THE ARCTIC OCEAN.

I WANT TO GO INVESTIGATE IT, BUT I THINK I MIGHT BE TOO OLD TO GO IT ALONE.

ARE YOU SAYING YOU NEED SOMEONE TO HELP YOU SAIL AROUND THE WORLD ON THE ADVENTURE OF A LIFETIME?

I DON'T JUST WANT *SOMEONE* TO COME WITH ME, STANLEY, I WANT IT TO BE *YOU.*

STAN O' WAR

215

EVERYONE, I HAVE AN ANNOUNCEMENT TO MAKE.

ME AND MY, *HEH*, NERDY BRO OVER HERE HAVE SOME CATCHIN' UP TO DO. WE'RE GONNA BE AWAY FOR A WHILE.

THAT'S WHY I'M SHUTTING DOWN THE MYSTERY SHACK FOR GOOD!

GASP

YOU SHUT DOWN YOUR MOUTH FOR GOOD!

I'M SORRY, MR. PINESES, IT'S JUST THAT THE SHACK IS THE MOST *MAGICAL* PLACE ON EARTH.

SURE, THE ATTRACTIONS ARE ALL FAKE, BUT DREAMS AREN'T FAKE.

LIKE THIS MERMAID—IT'S NOT JUST A DEAD FISH BUTT SEWN TO A MONKEY CARCASS, IT'S A MARVELOUS CREATURE THAT MAKES US BELIEVE THAT ANYTHING IS POSSIBLE.

YOU SHUT DOWN THIS SHACK, AND YOU SHUT DOWN OUR *DREAMS*.

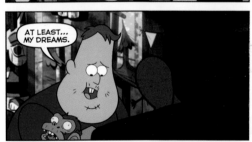

AT LEAST... MY DREAMS.

AWWW.

⊰SNIFF⊱ ⊰SOB⊱

AH, I'M SORRY, SOOS, IT'S JUST, THERE'S NO ONE AROUND TO RUN IT.

AT LEAST... THERE WOULDN'T BE IF I HADN'T JUST FOUND THE *PERFECT* REPLACEMENT.

LADIES AND GENTLEMEN, THE MYSTERY SHACK IS UNDER NEW MANAGEMENT!

WA-HOO! YEAH!

YOU-YOU MEAN IT, MR. MYSTERY?

YOU'RE MR. MYSTERY NOW, SOOS. TRY NOT TO BURN THE PLACE DOWN.

I'LL MOVE IN IMMEDIATELY.

WA-HOO!

YAY!

YAY!

LATER...

DO YOU *REALLY* HAVE TO GO?

THERE'S STILL SO MUCH WE HAVEN'T DONE TOGETHER.

WHAT? BUT IT'S LIKE, EIGHTY-SOMETHING DEGREES OUT TODAY.

CAN IT, SOOS!

GOODBYE STAN

HA-HA-HA-HA!

COOL

HEY, YOU MEAN A LOT TO ME, MAN.

YOU TOO.

UGH!

SOMETHING TO REMEMBER ME BY.

221

OH, AND THIS.

to:
Dipper

READ IT THE NEXT TIME YOU MISS GRAVITY FALLS.

SPEEDY BEAVER

LAST BUS LEAVING GRAVITY FALLS. ALL ABOARD.

GUESS WE'VE SAID GOOD-BYE TO EVERYONE, EXCEPT...

...WADDLES.

I-I DON'T KNOW HOW TO EXPLAIN THIS, BUT...UGH.

MOM AND DAD WON'T LET ME BRING A PIG HOME TO CALIFORNIA, SO... YOU HAVE TO STAY HERE.

OINK OINK?

COME ON, COME ON. I HAVE TO GO.

I'M ⸱SNIFF⸱ I'M SORRY, WADDLES.

RAAGHHH, YOU KNOW WHAT, FORGET IT!

I LIVED WITH THIS PIG ALL SUMMER, NOW *YOUR* PARENTS ARE GONNA HAVE TO.

HEY, BUS GUY, THIS PIG IS COMIN' WITH THE KIDS.

NOW, HOLD ON A SECOND. BRINGING ANIMALS ABOARD A MOVING VEHICLE IS STRICTLY PROHIBITED BY--

NO AN ALLO

--WAH. WE-WELCOME ABOARD! YOU CAN SIT IN THE FRONT ROW, PIG.

KIDS.

YOU KNUCKLEHEADS WERE NOTHIN' BUT A NUISANCE, AND I'M GLAD TO BE RID OF YA.

:SNIFF: WE'LL MISS YOU, TOO, GRUNKLE STAN.

READY TO HEAD INTO THE UNKNOWN?

NOPE. LET'S DO IT.

GRAVITY FALLS

CALIFORNIA

BYE! BYE!

TRAVEL SAFE!

BYE, DUDES!

BYE! BYE, EVERYBODY!

BYE! I'LL MISS YOU GUYS TOO!

REAVER

GRAVITY FALLS

"IF YOU'VE EVER TAKEN A ROAD TRIP THROUGH THE PACIFIC NORTHWEST, YOU'VE PROBABLY SEEN A BUMPER STICKER FOR A PLACE CALLED GRAVITY FALLS."

WELL, I'VE MOVED IN.

"IT'S NOT ON ANY MAPS. AND MOST PEOPLE HAVE NEVER HEARD OF IT.

"SOME PEOPLE THINK IT'S A MYTH.

"BUT IF YOU'RE CURIOUS...DON'T WAIT."

AAAHHHH!

"TAKE A TRIP.

RRRRRRGHHH

HRGH!

AGH!

"FIND IT.

HA-HA-HA!

STAN O'WAR II

"IT'S OUT THERE, SOMEWHERE IN THE WOODS. WAITING."

17-23-11-19 . 15-5
9-2-19-6,   23-10-20
15   1-9-10

15   23-12-1-23-25-5
12-9-2-19
21-9-6-6-3-8-4-15-10-17
12-15-2-19-5

10-9-1 15-4'5
4-15-11-19   4-9
5-4-23-6-4
4-16-19 18-3-10

10-9-1 12-19-4'5
5-19-19 1-16-15-21-16
8-15-10-19-5
5-3-6-2-15-2-19-5

1-16-19-10 9-10-19
17-19-4-5
4-6-23-8-8-19-20
15-10-5-15-20-19
4-16-19   8-23-5-4

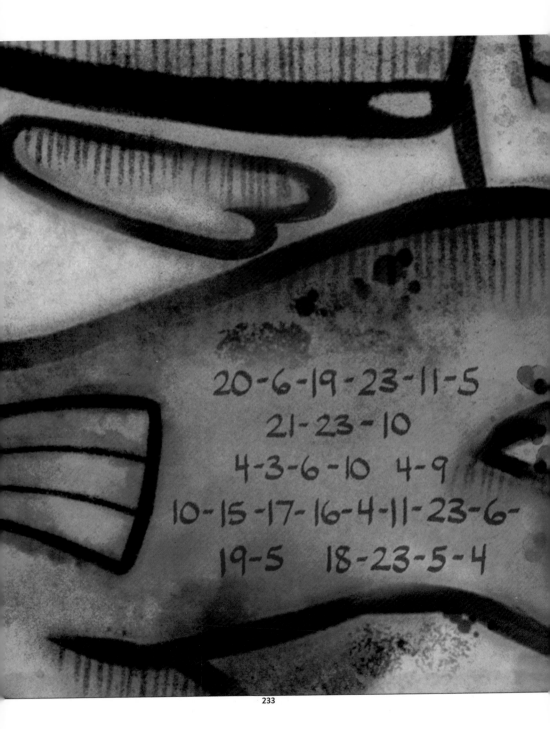

20-6-19-23-11-5
21-23-10
4-3-6-10 4-9
10-15-17-16-4-11-23-6-
19-5 18-23-5-4

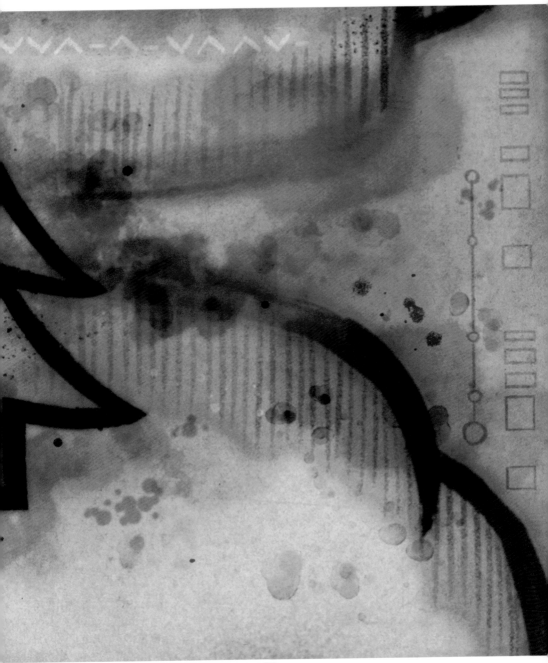

4-19-10 5-25-11-22-9-12-5
8-12-23-21-19-20 23-6-9-3-10-20
23 1-16-19-19-12

22-3-4 22-6-19-23-13 4-16-19
21-16-23-15-10, 23-10-20 8-23-25
4-16-19 21-9-5-4

16-23-10-20 15-10 16-23-10-20
4-16-19-25'12-12 22-9-10-20
4-16-19 5-19-23-12

4-16-19 8-6-9·8-16-19-21-25
1-15-12-12 23-12-12
22-19 12-9-5-4

CREDITS

WEIRDMAGEDDON PART 1

CREATED BY BILL CIPHER

Executive Producer: Alex Hirsch
Supervising Producer: Rob Renzetti
Art Director: Ian Worrel
Writers: Josh Weinstein and Alex Hirsch
Director: Sunil Hall

WEIRDMAGEDDON 2: ESCAPE FROM REALITY

CREATED BY BILL CIPHER

Executive Producer: Alex Hirsch
Supervising Producer: Rob Renzetti
Art Director: Ian Worrel
Writers: Jeff Rowe and Alex Hirsch
Director: Matt Braly

Weirdmageddon 3: Take Back the Falls

Created by Alex Hirsch

Executive Producer: Alex Hirsch
Supervising Producer: Rob Renzetti
Art Director: Ian Worrel
Writers: Shion Takeuchi, Mark Rizzo, Jeff Rowe,
Josh Weinstein, and Alex Hirsch
Director: Stephen Sandoval